DUDE

IT'S BAAACK.

NO 2

THE BOOK OF CRAZY, IMMATURE STUFF!

WRITE! DRAW! DESTROY!

SCHOLASTIC INC.
New York Toronto London Auckland
Sydney Mexico City New Delhi Hong Kong

Check it, bro. You're about to enter an abyss of pure "dude-dom".

STROY!

It's frightening, funny, and frighteningly funny. And of course, super cool.

No, it's fight, claw, deploy!

Ask your friends some ridunkulous questions. Make your bathroom way more interesting. Create a Mutant smackdown. Turn your filthy feet into a work of art.

Beware. Once you're in, there's no turning back.

DUDE No. 2 is powerful stuff!

Written and designed by
Mickey & Cheryl Gill

ISBN 978-0-545-43500-0

12 11 10 9 8 7 6 5 4 3 2 1   12 13 14 15 16 17/0

Printed in China   84

First Scholastic printing, January 2012

Reading cont
cause perm
loss of norr

WARNING
Flipping through
pages may trigger
noxious gas.

Thanks to Nik & Kirk Kaldor for bravely
testing these pages.

These signs do not
cover all dangers that
could happen while
reading this book.

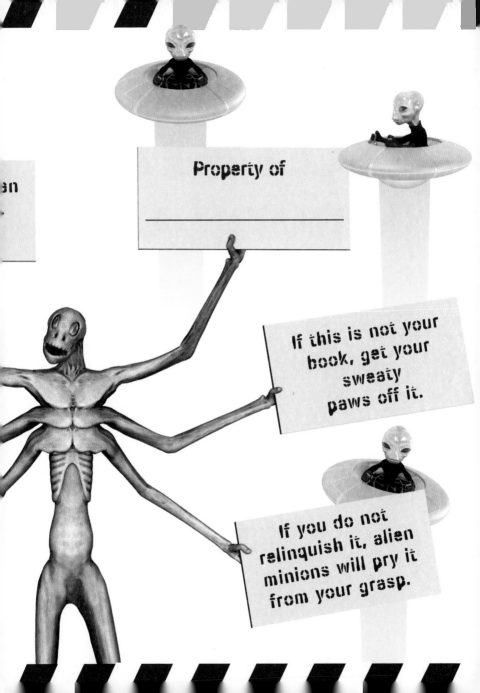

Are there Mutants among us?

scientific definition of mutation –
(myoō′tā shən)
noun

the changing of the structure of a gene, resulting in a variant form that may be transmitted to subsequent generations, caused by the alteration of single base units in DNA, or the deletion, insertion, or rearrangement of larger sections of genes or chromosomes.

dude definition of mutation –

something weird that happens inside and can make you super cool!

Sometimes they disguise themselves as average dudes like this.

You may already know some.

Turn the next page.

To find out,
friends, family

(If anyone, including you, answers "yes" to one or more of these questions, watch out.)

Can you

touch your tongue to your nose**?**
☐ yes ☒ no

pop your thumb out of joint**?**
☒ yes ☐ no

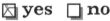
C'mon wiggle! wiggle your ears**?**
☐ yes ☒ no

touch your toes to your head**?**
☒ yes ☐ no

ask yourself,
teachers, etc.

make one eye look in a different direction than the other ?

☒ yes ☒ no

lift one eyebrow and not the other ?

☒ yes ☐ no

Ech.

bend just the top of a finger ?

☒ yes ☒ no

Make notes of any other weird things people you know can do.

Seriously dude, which ~~for-real~~ cool Mutant powers would you want?

Check all that apply.

Don't be greedy, dude.

- ☒ sprout wings from shoulder blades to fly
- ☒ turn your own flesh into steel
- ☐ send blasts of energy from eyes
- ☐ read people's minds
- ☐ control people's minds
- ☐ take on the form of ice/create ice
- ☐ control all forms of magnetism
- ☒ send fire blasts of energy
- ☐ absorb other Mutants' memories and powers
- ☐ control weather with your mind
- ☒ release claws from beneath the knuckles of each hand
- ☒ turn sonic vibrations into light, holograms, and laser-like cutting beams
- ☐ morph into anything you can imagine

Mega Mutant Power Standoff

Ask other dudes — if these Mutant powers went head to head, which would win?

Then pick a final winner.

Mutant Power #1		Mutant Power #2
Elongate body with unlimited range	VS.	Draw magnetic power from negative energy
Levitate own body and other matter with telekinetic powers	VS.	Possess armored body able to withstand extreme temperatures
Copy powers, IQ, fighting skills, and appearance of anyone around	VS.	Produce sonic scream to fly by, create deafening noise, and stun

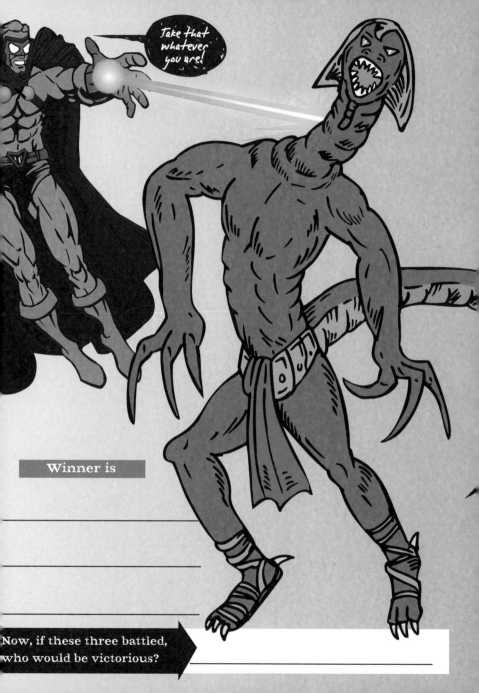

Rise of a New

Create your very own being with a Mutant gene. Here's a profile sheet to fill out. And don't forget to attach a picture to the file.

Mutant name _____

Real name _____

Birthplace _____

Citizen of _____
(country)

Occupation _____
(when not doing Mutant stuff)

Physical Appearance:

Height _____   Weight _____

Eye Color _____   Hair Color _____

Mutant traits _____
(like blue skin)

Powers _____

Accessories _____
(protective masks, etc.)

Mutant

Dude,
you are
a genius.

MISSING

Laugh your head off.

PARTS!

Add some not-so-obvious bodies to each of these.

HEADS UP!

These guys have lost their heads.
Draw new heads and keep it weird.

HAVE YOU EVER...

wanted your own pet monkey? ◯ No way! ◯ Oh yeah!

broken something during a sports game?
◯ No ◯ Yes. What? _____

put something besides your finger up your nose?
◯ No ◯ Yes. What? _____

blamed someone else for your fart? ◯ No way! ◯ Yes way.

given someone a wedgie? ◯ No ◯ Ha! Yes!

communicated with aliens from space ◯ Never ◯ Of course

taken the blame for someone else? ◯ No ◯ Yes

stepped in dog poo? ◯ Never ◯ Ugh, yes.

been sent to the principal's office? ◯ Yep ◯ Nope

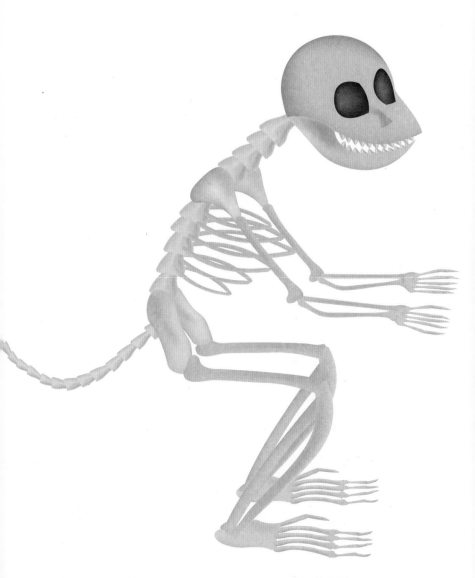

TURN PAGE FOR PULL-OUT GAME!

Spitball
Target Practice

LEAST FAVORITE CLASS
Gym

CHICK FLICKS

POP QUIZ

BRING

CHORES

SOCKS FOR BIRTHDAY

GETTING IN TROUBLE

SMOOTH JAZZ

BEING GROUNDED

GS HIT WITH PITBALL

TER BOX

OTTEN GGS

GGS

PUBL BATHR

DOG BR

HOURS 4 H OF HOME

APOLOGIZING AFTER BURPING

ARMPITS

SISTER OR BROTHER

COOKING
BRUSSELS SPROUTS

MAGICKING
ALLOWED 2 GAME
WHEN I'M NOT

#2

Supplies:
target
straw
paper
spit

1. PULL THIS TARGET OUT OF BOOK.

2. TAPE TO WALL.

3. LOCK IN ON SOMETHING YOU THINK STINKS, AIM, FIRE!

PRINT MORE TARGETS AT THEDUDEBOOK.COM/TARGETS

← TURN PAGE FOR PULL-OUT GAME!

Cut out or download staches from thedudebook.com. Tape to face and wear around.

WHAT'S

O a clown O

SCARIER,

R **a wooden dummy**
sitting on your
shelf in your
bedroom
at night

Look Ted!
More
wood!

This is epic!

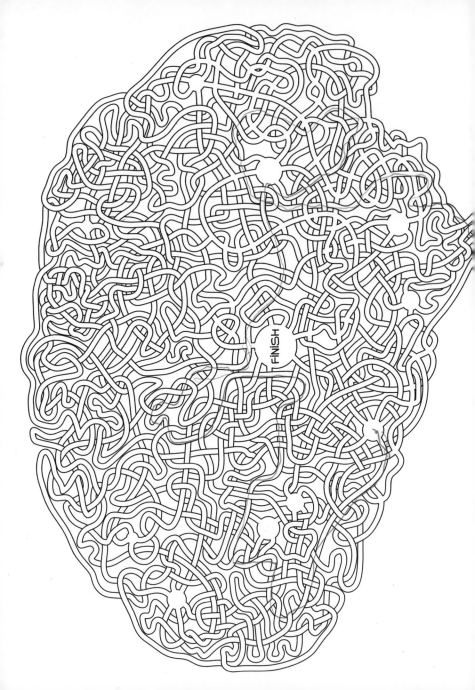

A MIND IS A TERRIBLE THING TO WASTE.

SO HERE IS A SUPER HARD MAZE THAT'S MADE OUT OF ONE!

USE YOUR BRAIN TO MAKE YOUR WAY THRU IT.

IT WILL DRIVE YOU MAD!

EVER FEEL LIKE SOME STUFF IS SO NOT FAIR?

Things could be worse. You COULD be a dung beetle.

EXTREME SPORTS. ULTIMATE FIGHTING. THAT'S OLD NEWS, DUDE. BRACE YOURSELF FOR

ATHLETICUS MAXIMUS!

IT'S HAZARDOUS, HIGH RISK, AND OFF-THE-CHARTS ADVENTUROUS.

I. COMBINE TWO OR MORE OF THESE SPORTS AND ACTIVITIES TO CREATE YOUR OWN SPORTING EVENT. (OR USE SOME NOT LISTED.)

BASKETBALL	DIVING	HANG GLIDING
BASEBALL	FOOTBALL	ROCK CLIMBING
RUGBY	WRESTLING	SNOWSHOEING
SOCCER	ARCHERY	SKI JUMPING
FIELD HOCKEY	GOLFING	MOTORCROSS
ICE HOCKEY	BOWLING	RACE CAR DRIVING
LACROSSE	SKATEBOARDING	BUNGEE JUMPING
TENNIS	SURFING	FRISBEE
RACQUETBALL	INLINE SKATING	POLE VAULTING
TRACK	WATER SKIING	BOXING
SWIMMING	SNOW SKIING	KARATE

TURN THE PAGE

2. LIST SOME OF YOUR WACK SPORTING EVENT COMBOS HERE. ASK SOME FRIENDS FOR THEIR COMBOS.

_____   _____

_____   _____

_____   _____

_____   _____

Bungee jump diving. Oh yeah!

3. NOW, MAKE YOUR ATHLETIC CHALLENGE EVEN MORE DANGEROUS. CHOOSE AN ANNOYING OBSTACLE FOR YOUR SPORT.

COMPETE IN MUD, ICE, OR FALLING GREEN SLIME

CROWD THROWS ROTTEN EGGS AT ATHLETES

FROGS LEAP THROUGH ATHLETES' LEGS

Alright! Hang glide archery while being pelted with green slime!

FLOCK OF CROWS FLY IN EVERY FIVE MINUTES

COMPETE ON FAST-MELTING, ICE-COVERED INLET FULL OF SHARKS

SPORTING AREA IS COVERED WITH MOUSETRAPS

GORILLA TROOP JUMPS IN AND OUT OF GAME

4. ADD AN OBSTACLE TO YOUR BEST SPORTING EVENT COMBO AND YOU HAVE A TOTALLY MAXIMUM SPORT, MAN!

_____

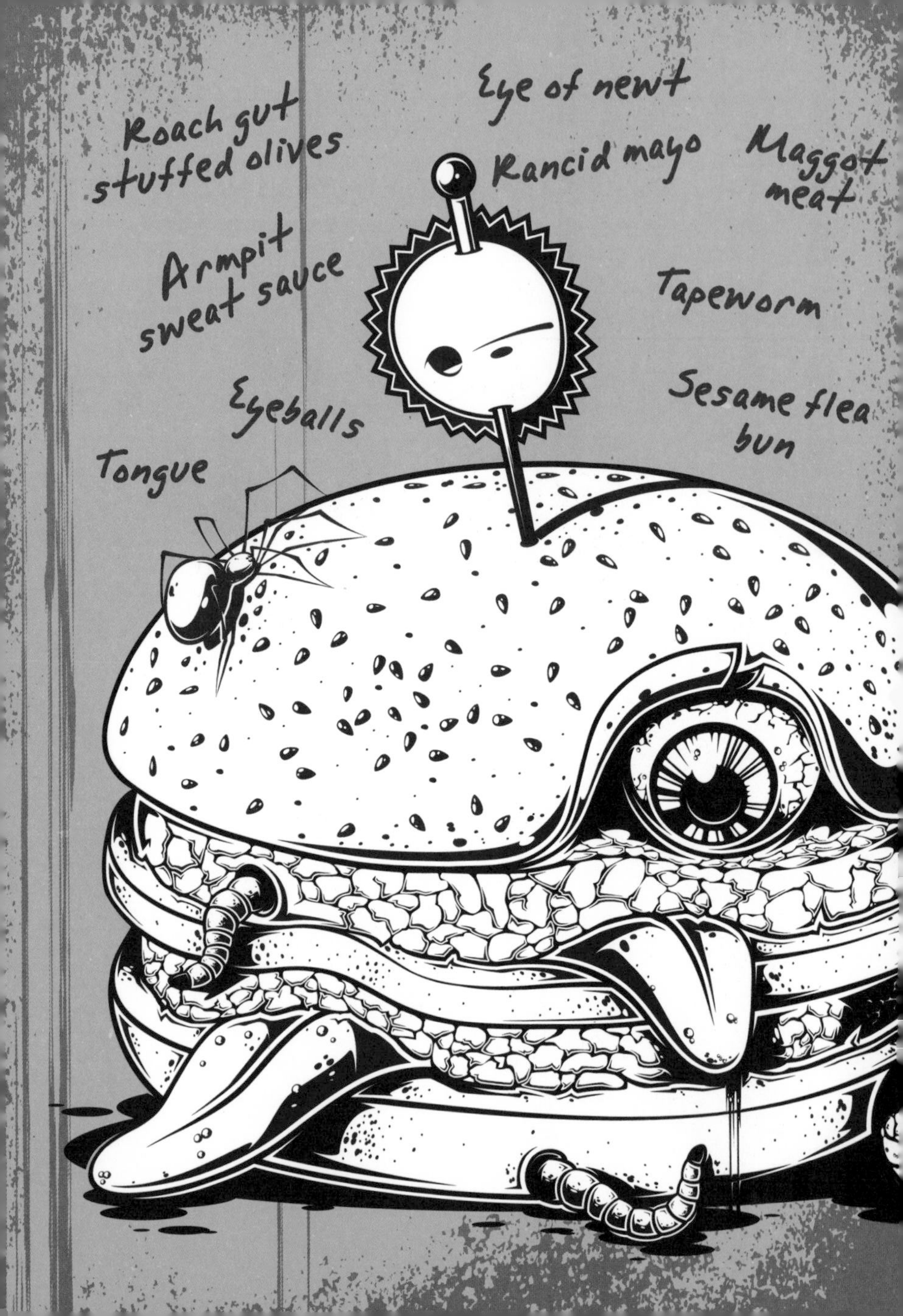
Eye of newt
Roach gut stuffed olives
Rancid mayo
Maggot meat
Armpit sweat sauce
Tapeworm
Eyeballs
Sesame flea bun
Tongue

BUILD A BARF-inducing BURGER!

Go to that gross part of the brain.
Think really hard. List all your
disgusting ingredients.

GROSS PART OF THE BRAIN

_____   _____

_____   _____

_____   _____

_____   _____

_____   _____

Rename

everyone in your family
you can think of.
Include yourself.

Old name	Way cooler, new name
_____	_____
_____	_____
_____	_____
_____	_____
_____	_____

Old name	Way cooler, new name
_____	_____
_____	_____
_____	_____
_____	_____
_____	_____
_____	_____
_____	_____
_____	_____
_____	_____

Great Aunt Bottle Rocket.

BIG

Help Sasquash blend in.
Draw your fave T-shirt or baseball
cap on him. Give him a smart phone,
earbuds and other cool gear.

(MAINLY ADULTS)
TO BUG PEOPLE

WHEN PEOPLE ASK YOU TO DO SOMETHING FOR THEM, ASK THEM ...

Would you like fries with that?

AFTER YOU PLACE A DRIVE-THRU ORDER, ASK ...

Can I micro-size that?

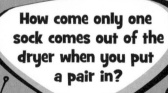

Have you seen (insert your own name) today? I can't find him anywhere. And he was just right here.

How come only one sock comes out of the dryer when you put a pair in?

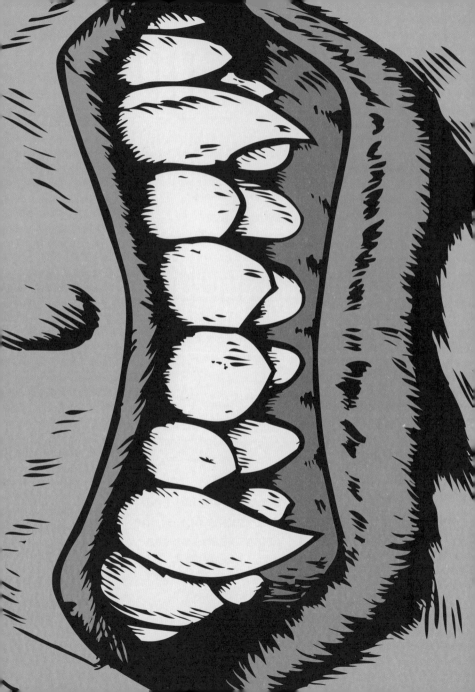

This is
the green GIANT.

But he's not too jolly. He has a toothache that needs some attention. Do you -

Does the name David Banner mean anything to you?

○ run screaming for your life

○ agree to find him a dentist who has gigantic dental equipment

○ ask your mom to give him something for the pain

○ get some rope, a truck, and a wild teenager (to drive the truck) and attempt to pull the tooth out

MAKE A

Ever wonder who the first dudes were that made the words — cool, awesome, epic, bro, and dude — so popular? Why can't you be the dude who starts using a really great word or phrase?
Now you can.

Bro, that's really Awesometacular!

Put a pen or pencil to paper and come up with your own.
Use them with your friends. The words or phrases might catch on.

If you get stumped, try combining some words together.

WORD OR PHRASE _Popular!_

New words

_____
_____
_____
_____
_____
_____
_____
_____

New phrases

_____
_____
_____
_____
_____
_____
_____
_____

i'm superepic fast!

Dude, Awesometastic is way better.

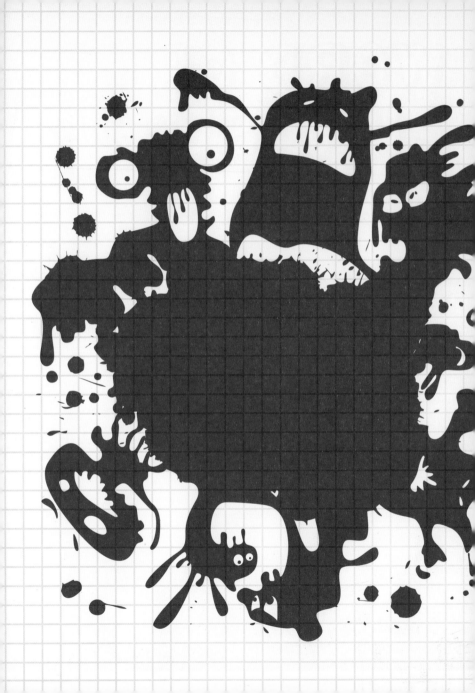

STINK BLOB TEST

- Show the STINK BLOB to friends, family, and random kids at school. Ask each person "What's the 1st word that enters your mind when you see this?" Record their answers here. Flip page upside down for revealing info.

Name	Word
_____	_____
_____	_____
_____	_____
_____	_____
_____	_____
_____	_____
_____	_____
_____	_____

If the person answered —

MONSTER - Wow! How original . . . not!

BLOB - This is a little better than "monster" but not much.

INK - This person probably does not want to take the test. Move on.

SCREAM, SCARY or HORROR - You've got yourself a deep thinker.

E.T. Invasion!

Ask a friend to give you a word OR choose one word from a group of words.

Choose one word:
billy goat, talking mole, giant peach

a room or area inside or outside your house

kitchen utensil you use to cook with

a gross noun

something with wheels

place you visit throughout the week

an animal and set of its body parts *(for example, mouse ears)*

something from a hardware store

Write his or her answers here.

1 _____

2 _____

3 _____

4 _____

5 _____

6 _____

7 _____

8 _____

something of yours you don't really like

_____ 9

Fill in the blanks with the correct words. Read your story out loud.

A _____ from outer space lands in/on your _____ .
1   2

You grab a _____ and approach it. He demands that you bring him
3

_____ so he can eat. You jump in/on your _____ and go
4   5

to a _____ to see if they have any _____ .
6   4

for your E.T. You're in shock! A green woman with _____ goes into the back
7

to get a _____ to help reach the _____ .
8   4

You get the _____ and return home, only to find that the _____ has
4   1

grown tired of waiting and has grabbed your _____ and is taking off in his ship.
9

Someday, you might have to travel everywhere giving interviews because you invented something really cool, discovered a cure for a disease, achieved world peace, hit the most home runs, or just really rocked out on your guitar.

First, you'll need an entourage.

entourage
ändtoō rä zh
noun
a group of people attending or surrounding an important person

Pick some people like friends, family, or dudes you would like to work for you. Write their names and jobs below. (Some great jobs might be buying new games for you or making sure you have a warm towel when you get out of the shower.)

Name	Job
_____	_____
_____	_____
_____	_____
_____	_____
_____	_____
_____	_____
_____	_____

**Second, you'll need a way to travel.
Choose one:**

- ○ Fleet of sports cars
- ○ Group of motorcycles
- ○ Tricked-out RV
- ○ Plane

Finally, you'll need some annoying creature comforts (stuff you just can't live without like a PB and banana sandwich with a chocolate malt every day). Don't worry about being too demanding, dude – it's what your entourage is for!

Make a list of food, activities, and things that would make traveling way better.

_____

_____

_____

_____

_____

_____

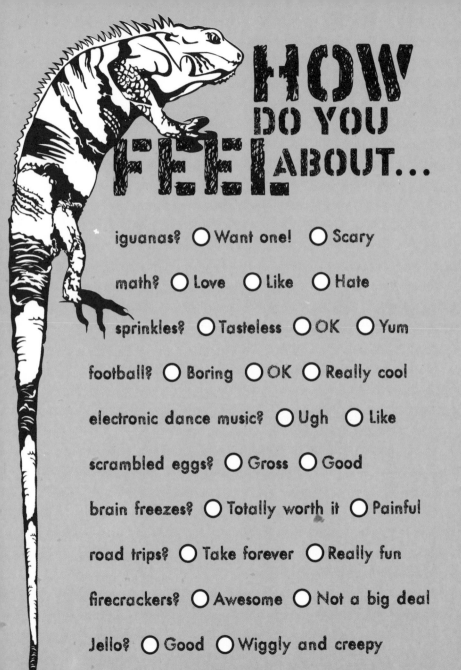

HOW
DO YOU
FEEL ABOUT...

iguanas? ○ Want one! ○ Scary

math? ○ Love ○ Like ○ Hate

sprinkles? ○ Tasteless ○ OK ○ Yum

football? ○ Boring ○ OK ○ Really cool

electronic dance music? ○ Ugh ○ Like

scrambled eggs? ○ Gross ○ Good

brain freezes? ○ Totally worth it ○ Painful

road trips? ○ Take forever ○ Really fun

firecrackers? ○ Awesome ○ Not a big deal

Jello? ○ Good ○ Wiggly and creepy

Does Your LAST NAME Ever Bother You?

Maybe it begins with an "A" so you're the first kid to give a book report. Or your name's Zithers and you sweat for three days waiting to give your book report.

Either way, here's your chance to change it. The result might be better, and it might not be.

GO FOR IT, DUDE!

Whew, now I can lose the disguise.

1. Choose name generator A or Z.

2. Select a letter from each column and enter it in the box below it.

Name Generator A

B	R	O	M	A	S
C	L	U	P	E	T

☐ ☐ ☐ ☐ ☐ ☐

Name Generator Z

W	O	C	N	E	K
Z	U	P	K	A	T
					S

☐ ☐ ☐ ☐ ☐ ☐

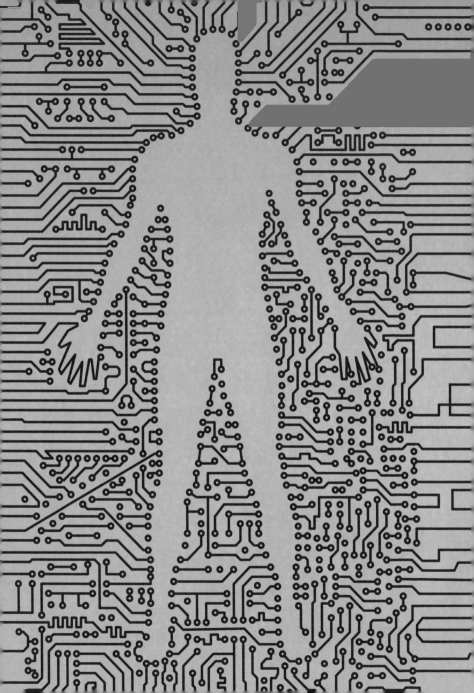

BIONIC DUDE

Scientists can make you stronger, faster, and just way more awesome.

CHOOSE YOUR ELECTROMECHANICAL PARTS:

REPLACE YOUR EYE WITH ONE THAT

- ○ SEES IN THE DARK
- ○ HAS INCREDIBLY PRECISE TARGETING POWER WHEN THROWING OBJECTS
- ○ TAKES PHOTOS WITH EACH BLINK

IMPLANT ONE ARM WITH

- ○ MAJOR STRENGTH TECHNOLOGY
- ○ ROCKET LAUNCHER
- ○ SUPER EXTENSION LINKS

ADD A CIRCUIT SYSTEM TO LEGS FOR

- ○ SUPERHUMAN SPEED
- ○ OFF-THE-CHARTS LEAPING POWER

NO SYSTEM IS PERFECT. INCLUDING YOURS. CHOOSE AN ELECTRICAL CIRCUIT INTERFERENCE.

- ○ COLD WEATHER SLOWS FUNCTIONS DOWN
- ○ RAIN COMPLETELY DISABLES ABILITIES

SO YOU"RE IN CHARGE OF YOUR OWN PARALLEL UNIVERSE.

Wh
am

WHY NOT CHANGE IT UP? START WITH NUMBERS.
WHY USE THE SAME EXACT NUMBERS THAT
EVERYONE USES IN THAT OTHER UNIVERSE?
1,2,3,4, YAWN.

GIVE THESE NUMBERS SOME NEW NAMES AND NEW SYMBOLS.

(CHANGE THE NAME OF NUMBER 11 TO VORK. ITS NEW SYMBOL COULD BE ౚ.)

NEW NAME   NEW SYMBOL

1. _____   _____

2. _____   _____

3. _____   _____

4. _____   _____

5. _____   _____

6. _____   _____

7. _____   _____

8. _____   _____

9. _____   _____

10. _____   _____

A LITTLE GREEN MAN LANDED HIS SHIP NEXT TO A PHONE BOOTH IN A COW PASTURE BECAUSE HE NEEDED TO PHONE HOME.

Finally some excitement.

COME UP WITH THE NEXT LINE FOR THE STORY AND
WRITE IT BELOW. READ THE FIRST TWO LINES OF THE STORY
TO A FRIEND AND ASK HIM TO CONTINUE IT.
KEEP ASKING FRIENDS FOR MORE LINES UNTIL
YOU FINISH THE SCI-FI SAGA.

CONTINUE YOUR TALE HERE.

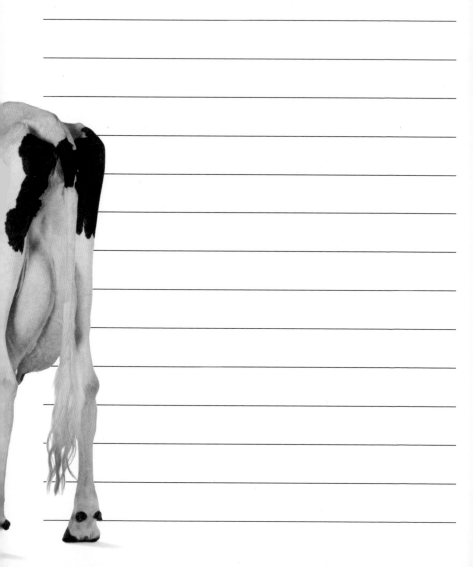

Don't know the answer when you're called on in class?

Sorry, I don't know the answer. I've been devoting my energy to an all-consuming math equation that might help mankind time travel. Just think of what we could do with that knowledge!

I'm experiencing a case of brain-cicles. I might remember the answer when everything thaws out. Check back with me tomorrow.

I do not currently have the answer. Any data stored in my brain resulting from studying has been extracted temporarily. It's being inserted into an automaton for experimentation.

automaton –
noun
a moving mechanical device made in imitation of a human being.

Forget GUINNESS.

start your own Book of

Longest balancin on bicycle

Cyclist's name and time

FEET CAN'T TOUCH THE GROUND, MAN!

Largest rubberband ball

Creator's name

Diameter of ball

Hold trials with your friends and family to see who's record-breaking material.

Local Records.

Farthest-flying paper airplane

_____
Creator's name

_____
Distance

Longest-holding handstand

_____
Handstander's name

_____
Time

Fastest 100 meter dash

_____
Runner's name

_____
Time

Most back-to-back basketball shots

_____
Player's name

_____
Shots made

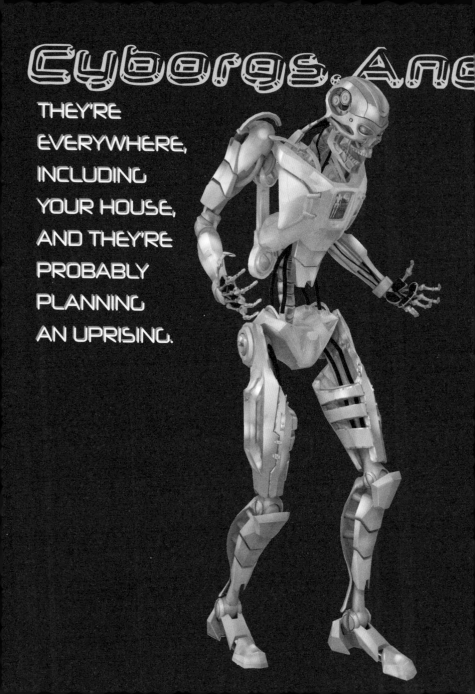

Cyborgs. And

THEY'RE
EVERYWHERE,
INCLUDING
YOUR HOUSE,
AND THEY'RE
PROBABLY
PLANNING
AN UPRISING.

aids. Robots.

Look for soap or lotion dispensers, spray bottles near the sink, or anything that looks robo-like. Draw it here. Add special parts to it to give it a Transformer or Star Wars General Grievous look.

YOU, YES YOU, HAVE THE AMAZING

ONCE-IN-A-LIFETIME OPPORTUNITY TO WORK ALONGSIDE WORLD-FAMOUS DR. SCI-FLY.

PART MAN, PART FLY, ALL MAD SCIENTIST.

1. PUT ON YOUR LAB COAT. IF YOU DON'T HAVE ONE, FLEX YOUR MENTAL MUSCLE AND ACT LIKE YOU DO. (THAT'S YOUR BRAIN, DUDE.)

2. COME UP WITH A NAME FOR YOURSELF. YOU KNOW, ALL "SCIENCEY" LIKE MR. SPOCK OR CREEPY LIKE DR. MOREAU OR DR. FRANKENSTEIN.

☐ MR.  check a box.

☐ DR.

☐ PROFESSOR

(YOUR SUPER COOL NAME)

I wish I were cool like Dr. Sci-Fly.

Well you're not. You are just a dung beetle. Go back to page 32.

3. NOW, CHOOSE YOUR EXPERIMENT.

☐ DESIGN A LASER-SHOOTING HELMET, WITH MEAN GUY HEAT VISION, FOR LLAMAS. UNLOAD A HERD OF THEM ON YOUR SCHOOL CAMPUS. IF YOU HAVE ANY HELMET MALFUNCTIONS, NO WORRIES. THEY CAN ALWAYS SPIT ON THE BULLIES. (IT'S ALWAYS SMART TO HAVE AN ORGANIC BACK-UP PLAN WHEN WORKING WITH ANIMALS.)

☐ INVENT THE LAZY BOY. NO, NO, A REAL LAZY BOY. NOT THAT CHAIR YOUR DAD SITS IN. IT WOULD DO EVERYTHING YOU DON'T HAVE TIME FOR. YOU ARE A SCIENTIST, AFTER ALL. IT BRUSHES YOUR TEETH, MAKES YOUR BED, WRITES AWESOME PAPERS. YOU GET THE PICTURE.

☐ TAP INTO BOTTLENOSE DOLPHINS' BRAIN WAVES, LEARN TO COMMUNICATE WITH THEM TELEPATHICALLY, AND DRAW UP PLANS TO TAKE OVER THE WORLD WITH DIABOLICAL DOLPHIN POWER.

5. SHARE YOUR PLANS WITH ONLY A FEW PEOPLE YOU REALLY TRUST. BE CAREFUL. THERE ARE PLENTY OF OTHER WILD INVENTORS OUT THERE JUST WAITING TO STEAL YOUR MEGA BRAIN IDEAS.

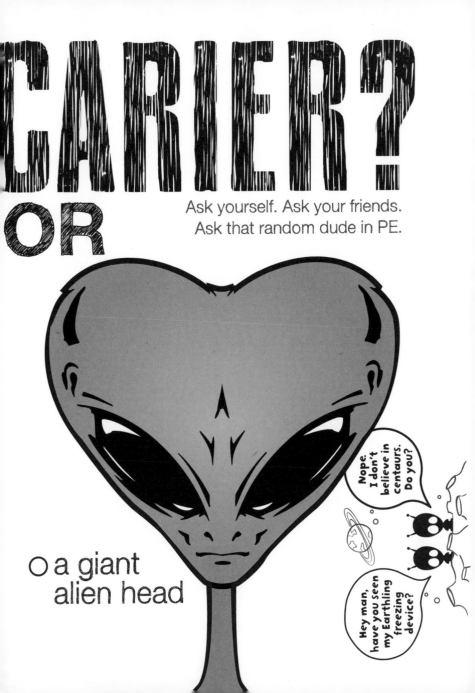

WHO WOULD YOU NOT WANT TO BE STUCK ON AN ELEVATOR WITH?

- a scary alien

Move over.

- suspicious-looking guy with a bunch of explosives

- kid with a tube of rash cream who won't stop scratching

- two-headed goat with really bad breath

- a kid who really needs to "go"
- gassy pig

- swarm of killer bees
- group of zombies

bunch of
- rats
- bats on the loose

○ musician who must play her ukulele

○ oboe to calm down

○ group of skateboarders who reek

○ rotting fish

○ hyper kid with a case of Red Bull

○ kid hiding in the corner

○ panicked girl who won't stop screaming

○ crying

○ angry gorilla

○ hungry boa constrictor

WHAT'S MORE AWESOME?

- ○ Downtown apartment
- ○ Beach condo

- ○ Chocolate chip cookie brownie combo
- ○ Spaghetti tacos

Wow, a talking babY?

Talking
- ○ dog
- ○ baby

Bedroom with
- ○ a covered bridge connecting to outdoor treehouse
- ○ an indoor slide leading to outdoor, infinity swimming pool with a hot tub and waterfall

- ○ Noncavity, nonsugar-rush, nonfat sugar
- ○ Coke-flavored medicine

- ○ Shoes with wings
- ○ Backpack with built-in, mini vending machine

- ○ You
- ○ Two of you

Your kitchen with
○ your own pizza chef
○ an ice cream shop in it

○ Gaming monkey
○ Laser tag playing kangaroo

Your own
○ private jet
○ hot air balloon

Anchovy pizza coming right up!

My cloak isn't working right.

Ugh.

Your favorite
○ T-shirt
○ shoes

○ Invisibility cloak
○ Magic wand

Living room with a
○ go-cart track
○ roller coaster looping thru it

○ Field trip
○ Day off from school

Sir, can I do your homework for you?

Your own
○ butler
○ chauffeur

○ Giant gaming room
○ Full-scale movie theater with concession area in your house

Coke or Pepsi?

Those buns on their heads and the diaper-thingies they wear are ridunkulous!

WHAT'S MOST HILARIOUS?

Sumo wrestler's

O body O topknot O outfit

O Waterskiing squirrel
O Surfing dog

Kowabunga!

People

O falling down
O messing up their words
O running into things

O Zipper down
O Toilet paper stuck
   to the shoe

O Underarm
O Mouth
O Smart phone farting

○ Dog dragging butt across carpet
○ Cat chasing tail

Talking
○ toilet
○ totem pole

Dude, what did you eat? Whew!

The animal name
○ pink fairy armadillo
○ spotted cuscus
○ Dumbo octopus

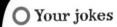

How 'bout
○ star-nosed mole
○ hagfish
○ sucker-footed bat

○ Your jokes
○ You trying to tell a joke

Coke or Pepsi?

IS IT YES OR NO?

ow.

Does biting a leg off an animal cookie bother you?
○ Kinda, it's creepy. ○ No

So tired.

Think you'll live to 100?
○ Yep
○ Nope

Yacked in a plane?
○ Ugh, yes.
○ No

How 'bout on a boat?
○ Yes
○ No

Do you keep wearing stinky sneakers?
○ Yes ○ Gross, no.

Scream on roller coasters? ◯ Yeah ◯ Nah

How 'bout at scary movies?

◯ No
◯ Depends
◯ Yes!

Know your best friend's middle name?

◯ No
◯ Yeah, it's _____

Is your second toe longer than your big toe?

◯ Yes
◯ No

Ever lost a toenail?

◯ Yep
◯ Huh?
◯ Nah

RIP THIS PAGE OUT OF THE BOOK.

LAY IT DOWN SOMEWHERE
OUTSIDE. PUT A ROCK OR
SOMETHING HEAVY ON IT
SO IT WON'T BLOW AWAY.
PICK IT UP ONE WEEK
LATER & TAPE BACK IN BOOK.

Cover
this
entire
page
with
anything
except
ink
or
lead.
Use
tape,
staples,
gum,
hair,
and
other
stuff.
Don't
leave
any
white
space.

Then
turn
these
boards
into
something
different
by
drawing
on
them.
(For
example,
you
could
turn
one
into
an
apartment
building
for
dust
mites.)

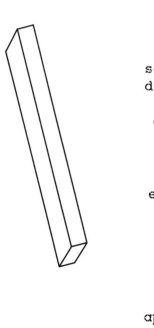

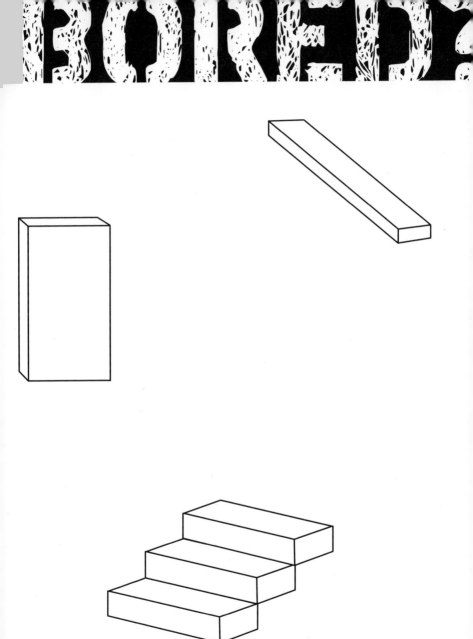

Still
bored?
Trace
your
dirty
toes
on
this
page.
Draw
faces
on
toe
outlines
to
create
monsters,
aliens,
heroes,
or a
group
of
tough
guys
with
names
like
"Nails"
or
"Ingrown".

Use all the extra white space on these pages to mak

What's
the
smallest
thing
you
can
think
of
?

Write
it
here.

a list of all the small stuff you can think of.

OK,
now
what's
the
smallest
thing you
can
think
of
AND
you
can
kinda
draw
?

Draw
it
here.

When
you
get
something
sticky
or
gross
on
your
hands,
feet,
or
wherever,
smear
it
on
this
page.
Date
it
and
label
what
you
think
it
is.

Substance 1

Substance 2

Substance 3

Substance 4

Can
you
capture
a stink?
Find
out.
Every
time
you
reek,
wipe
your
pits
and
sweat
on
this
page.
Smell
what
happens.

No one
will touch
your book!

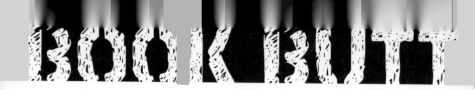

BOOK BUTT

Take
this
book
everywhere
you
go.
When
you
sit
down,
open
it
up
to
this
page,
face
page
down,
and
sit
on
it.
Keep
doing
it
until
the
paper
starts
picking
up
all
the
dirty
stuff
you
sit
on!

DRAW WITHOUT LOOKING

Grab
a
subject—
a
bro,
dude,
sis,
or
random
friend.
Draw
their
face
here ...
without
looking
down
at
the
page.

TASTY OR TERRIBLE?
MOUTHWATERING
OR DISGUSTING?

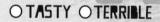
Lima beans & ketchup!

HAVE ANY WEIRD FOOD COMBOS YOU LOVE?
ASK FRIENDS FOR THEIR UNUSUAL MIXES.
MAKE A LIST OF THEM HERE.
THEN DECIDE IF THEY'RE GOOD OR BAD.

FOOD COMBO

_____   ○ TASTY   ○ TERRIBLE

_____   ○ YUM!   ○ YUCK!

_____   ○ DELISH   ○ NASTY

_____   ○ MOUTH-WATERING   ○ DISGUST-ING

_____   ○ I'D TRY IT.   ○ NO WAY!

_____   ○ AWESOME   ○ FOUL

_____   ○ LIP-SMACKING   ○ GROSS

They all look gross to me.

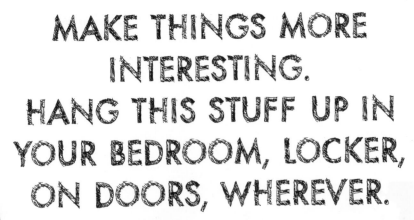

MAKE THINGS MORE INTERESTING.
HANG THIS STUFF UP IN YOUR BEDROOM, LOCKER, ON DOORS, WHEREVER.

Go to
THEDUDEBOOK.COM
to download more copies and other signs.

Hang on bedroom door.

ASK THE MASK OF KNOWLEDGE FOR ENTRY.

Write a number on a sticky note and place in the middle of sign. Hang on door.
(When you want to scare people, place a new sticky on the door with a really small number.)

THIS IS A ZOMBIE-FREE ROOM

IT HAS BEEN

Place
sticky note
here.

DAYS SINCE THE LAST FLESH-EATING INCIDENT.

W☠RNING

AVOID CONTACT WITH DOORKNOB. MAY CAUSE SKIN IRRITATION.

Hang on bedroom door.

⚠ WARNING

WEAR EYE PROTECTION

Exposure to my brilliant awesomeness may cause temporary blindness.

Deter vistors. Hang on bedroom door.

⚠ **DANGER**

FLYING SQUIRRELS
Full face shield required beyond this point.

DO NOT ENTER

MAY CAUSE MENTAL DEGRADATION

IF YOU DO NOT KNOW WHAT THIS MEANS, THEN YOU CLEARLY ALREADY TRESPASSED AND WILL BE PROSECUTED TO THE FULL EXTENT OF THE LAW.

Tape a photo of you, brother or sister to space below. Hang on bedroom door.

⚠ DANGER

DO NOT ENTER
THIS AREA
EXPERIMENT
IN SESSION

Tape
photo here

Hang on your bedroom door.

WARNING TO FAMILY

DO NOT TOUCH, LOOK AT, OR EVEN THINK ABOUT THE CONTENTS OF THIS ROOM.

TURN PAGE FOR PULL-OUT SIGN.

LOST MONSTER

Answers to Sweet Pea

Color: Mostly green with gray claws

Last seen in bathroom toilet _____

date

REWARD OFFERED IF BROUGHT BACK FED.

If you have any information,

please contact: _____

email address

TURN PAGE BACK FOR PULL-OUT SIGN.

TURN PAGE FOR PULL-OUT PRANK.

Cut on dotted lines and tape to roll of white toilet paper.

TURN PAGE BACK FOR PULL-OUT PRANK.

Check it, dude.
Direct your looking holes
to the blog at
thedudebook.com

AIR FARTER BOMBER